Make a New Friend in Jesus

PassAlong Arch® Books help you share Jesus with friends close to you and with children all around the world!

When you've enjoyed this story, pass it along to a friend. When your friend is finished, mail this book to the address below. Concordia Gospel Outreach promises to deliver your book to a boy or girl somewhere in the world to help him or her learn about Jesus.

Myself

My name _____

My address _____

_____

My PassAlong Friend

My name _____

My address _____

_____

When you're ready to give your PassAlong Arch® Book to a new friend who doesn't know about Jesus, mail it to

Concordia Gospel Outreach
3547 Indiana Avenue
St. Louis, MO 63118

PassAlong Series

Copyright © 1995 Concordia Publishing House
3558 S. Jefferson Avenue, St. Louis, MO 63118-3968
Manufactured in the United States of America

1 2 3 4 5 6 7 8 9 10   04 03 02 01 00 99 98 97 96 95

Jesus
and the
Little Children

Mark 9:33–37, 42;
10:13–16 for Children

Carol Greene
Illustrated by Michelle Dorenkamp

SAINT LOUIS

I'm just a child, some people think.
My head is full of play.
But I have ears and I can hear.
So come on over. Gather near.
I'll tell two tales today.

They're tales about the Jesus Man.
You've heard of Him before?
He traveled in these parts, you know,
God's ways to teach, God's love to show,
And more. Oh, yes! Much more.

"They're good tales. And they're true."

Capernaum's where the first tale starts,
Along the road to town.
A group of men came walking by,
Their ears were red, their voices high,
And each face wore a frown.

"Well, I'm the greatest," one man said.
"You see all that I do."
"Oh no you're not." "You're very wrong."
They argued as they walked along.
"I'm much more great than you."

"What a silly thing to argue about!"

Are not!" "Am too!" The fight went on
As if they didn't know
Behind them, weary to the bone,
Lord Jesus followed, all alone,
His footsteps tired and slow.

They came at last to someone's house
And knocked upon the door.
"Lord Jesus! Come on in! How grand!"
The householder took Jesus' hand.

"Jesus' visits must be special."

Inside, the family fed the Lord
And His disciples too.
"Our house is Yours. So please, Lord, stay
And rest a while. Don't rush away.
Here, have a bit more stew."

When all the food was gone and they
Were resting, Jesus said,
"What were you arguing about?"
His helpers blushed. No words came out,
And none would raise his head.

"I'm glad I don't blush."

But Jesus knew. "Whoever would
Be first, he must be last.
The greatest must be slave to all,
Instead of strutting, proud and tall."
Their eyes were still downcast.

Then Jesus hugged a little child.
"I show this child to you.
When you have welcomed him, you see
—a little child—you've welcomed Me,
And God the Father too.

"What a surprise for those disciples!"

But he who makes a small child sin
And turn away from Me—
It would be better for that wreck
To tie a stone around his neck
And throw him in the sea."

Do you know what Lord Jesus meant?
I'm pretty sure I know.
I think He wants us safe from harm.
He wants us happy, loved, and warm,
Because He loves us so.

"That's what I think too."

And when I think of all His love,
My smile gets ten feet wide.
When Jesus says He loves us so,
The joy you feel just has to show.
You can't keep it inside.

"Whoopee!"

It's later in Judea, that
My second tale takes place,
Where Jesus went to teach some more.
The crowds all gathered as before.
That always was the case.

And some drank in each word He spoke
And found all they desired,
While others liked to badger Him,
Their voices shrill, their faces grim.
They must have made Him tired.

"What a bunch of prune-pusses!"

At last He went into a house
To rest and maybe pray.
But outside still more folks drew near,
Their faces full of hope and fear.
Would He see them today?

It was a group of mothers who
Brought children there that day.
They were not asking very much,
Just for each child to feel His touch,
And then they'd go away.

"Will Jesus see them?"

And then disciples came outside,
    Their faces stern and grim.
    "The Lord has done enough today.
    So turn around and go away.
    You mustn't bother Him."

"Those MEANIES!"

^But we've brought children," said the moms,
"To feel Lord Jesus' touch.
You have no right to scowl and scold.
He welcomes children, we've been told,
And loves them very much."

"That's telling 'em!"

They're right," a voice said from the door
And Jesus stepped outside.
"They're right!" He looked so angry then,
If I had been one of those men,
I would have tried to hide.

"I'm teaching you important things
Before I go away.
I *said* each child is dear to Me.
I wonder if you'll ever see
The truth of what I say."

"So there!"

But angry as the Lord's words were,
The children were not scared.
"Come to Me, little ones," He said,
And laid His hands on each small head,
And each child knew He cared.

"See how much He cares!"

I don't know what the Lord did then.
Perhaps He went back in.
But if I'd been there, I know I
Would hug Him and I'd laugh and cry
And hug Him once again.

And then because He seemed so tired,
And maybe sad that day,
We'd play until His heart grew light.
We wouldn't mind the coming night.
I'd beg Him, "Stay, Lord! Stay!"

"Playing with children is good for grownups."